C000186982

So you want to be a PALAEONTOLOGIST?

Practical advice for fossil enthusiasts

of all ages

David Penney

SIRI SCIENTIFIC PRESS

ISBN 978-0-9929979-6-0
Published by Siri Scientific Press, Manchester, UK
This and related titles are available directly from the publisher at:

http://www.siriscientificpress.co.uk

© 2016, Siri Scientific Press. All rights reserved. No parts of this publication may be reproduced, stored in a retrieval system or transmitted, in any form or by any means, electronic, mechanical, photocopying, recording or otherwise, without the prior written permission of the publisher. This does not cover photographs and other illustrations provided by third parties, who retain copyright of their images; reproduction permissions for these images must be sought from the copyright holders. Creative Commons images are available online under the licenses specified in the figure legends.

Cover image: *Dinosaur excavation in the region of Aderbissinat, Thirozerine Dept., Agadez Region, Republic of Niger (from Remes et al. 2009, PLoS ONE 4(9): e6924)*

For

Amelia

The joy a baby brings is profound.
How bizarre that the child,
even when a parent itself,
has no recollection of
this great achievement.

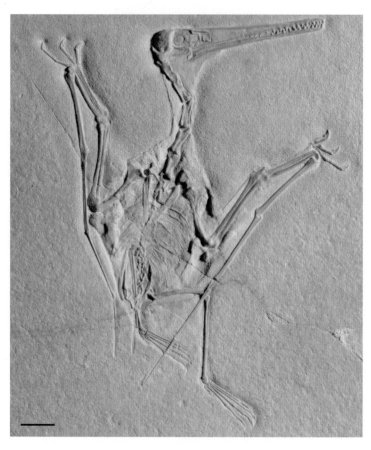

Pterosaur from the classic Upper Jurassic Solnhofen locality of Bavaria; scale bar = 20 mm (Vidovic & Martill 2014, PLoS ONE 9(10): e110646)

CONTENTS

The author on the Jurassic coast of Lyme Regis,
with a rock packed full of ammonites

Preface

Palaeontology is a rather unique career choice, in that at one point or another most kids (and some adults) want to be a palaeontologist, but very few of them are ever able to realize their dream. However, I expect there are more avenues into palaeontology related work today than there ever have been and the main purpose of this book is to highlight some of the potential routes into palaeontology as a career, or as a more productive pastime than just basic fossil collecting. I wanted the book to be accessible to as broad an audience as possible, from primary school children (or at least their parents) up to those who may be in retirement. After all, it is never too early nor too late to pursue your palaeontological passion!

There are not many things I remember about my early childhood, but some events I can recollect with vivid clarity. I do remember being infatuated with dinosaurs. I do recall standing in my primary school playground trying to imagine the size of a *Brachiosaurus* stood next to a large oak tree in the school grounds. I can see the pages of my favourite dinosaur book in my mind's eye, but most importantly of all, I can vividly recall exactly how I lost total interest in dinosaurs before I was even ten-years-old!

This would have been the mid-1970s when I was about eight-years-old. My favourite dinosaur book had no photographs, but was nicely illustrated with reconstructions of the dinosaurs, the habitats in which they once lived and of people at excavations recovering the fossilized bones from the ground. My imagination ran wild at the idea of finding my own dinosaur fossils, or at least seeing the real thing in the field. Hence, I asked my mother if we could go and see some dinosaur fossils. She explained that the fossils illustrated in the book came from North America and Canada, and that it would require a very long aeroplane flight (from the UK) in order to get there, and that such a trip was not a realistic possibility. I was devastated. As a young child, I wanted to get 'hands on', not just to learn from books, and so my passion for dinosaurs waned rapidly in favour of the multitude of easily accessible spiders and insects in a vacant area of grassland opposite our home.

At this time, few people were aware of the rich dinosaur heritage of the UK, a situation now rectified by an excellent book on *Dinosaurs of the British Isles* by Dean Lomax and Nobumichi Tamura (2014), the recent (2015) TV documentary *Dinosaur Britain* and of course via information available on the internet. Had this knowledge been commonplace when I was a child then I expect I would have retained my palaeontological interests and developed them accordingly. It wasn't, so my interest in the tangible and accessible local bug fauna flourished and my knowledge about them increased tremendously as a result of reading books but also through collecting and studying them in the field. Obviously, I had no idea at the time that these childhood buggy exploits would set the groundwork for a future career in palaeontology.

I completed an undergraduate degree in Zoology at the University of Manchester and graduated in 1994, just one year following the release of the blockbuster movie *Jurassic Park*. This movie had increased awareness of amber and interest in it as a remarkable medium in which delicate insects and other organisms are preserved as fossils with startling life-like fidelity. Moreover, there was a lecturer at the university who was an expert on fossil spiders preserved in rock and who was looking for a PhD student to undertake

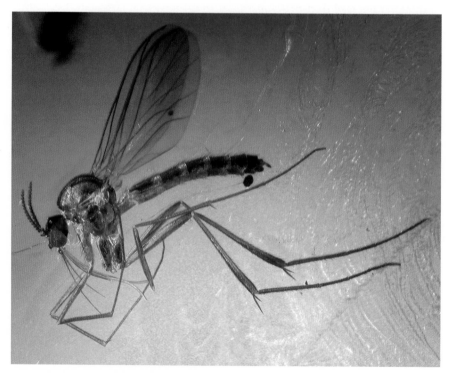

Long-beaked fungus gnat in 16 million-year-old Miocene amber from the Dominican Republic

*Tube-web spider in 44–49 million-year-old Eocene amber
from the Baltic region*

research on spiders preserved in amber. He was aware of my existence and interest in spiders as a result of my long-term membership of the *British Arachnological Society*, and so he sought me out for a chat and that initiated my research on fossil spiders preserved in amber. The obvious conclusion here is that I just happened to be in the right place at the right time. It is true. There was no great master plan on my part, everything just naturally fell into place. If you take the time to search for biographies online you will see that the same is true for plenty of other palaeontologists out there. It is rather surprising how many of them use the word 'luck' when describing their particular route into studying fossils for a living.

I now have a PhD and also a higher doctorate (DSc, recently submitted) in palaeontology, despite having left school with just two O'levels (GCSE equivalent) and having failed my O'level course in geology twice! Actually, the second time around I turned up for the exam the day after it had happened. Throughout my career to date I have been a laboratory

The author presenting a Keynote lecture at a scientific conference in Germany, 2013

technician, a PhD student, a museum curator, a post-doctoral researcher and now run a publishing business focused on palaeontology. I have done interviews for online media, radio and television and have been filmed about my research for a number of TV documentaries. I have traded in fossils (online and at fossil fairs), have given talks to primary school children and other community groups, as well as for learned societies and at international conferences (often as an invited Keynote Speaker). I have also held various honorary positions and currently conduct my research as an Honorary Lecturer at the University of Manchester. My research interests are broad and include many of the sub-disciplines mentioned in the next section, including invertebrate palaeontology, palaeobiology, taphonomy, virtual palaeontology, palaeobiogeography and molecular palaeontology.

The author collecting amber in Lebanon, 2003

I have travelled the world extensively as a result of my palaeontological research, whether it be to collect fossils in the field, examine museum collections or to attend conferences. In 2004, my research took me to the

Dinosaurs on display at the Royal Tyrrell Museum of Palaeontology, Alberta, Canada (Steven Mackaay, Wikimedia CC BY-SA 3.0)

Royal Tyrrell Museum of Palaeontology in the sleepy town of Drumheller, Alberta, Canada, to study their collection of fossil insects in Canadian amber. The museum is situated in the middle of the fossil-bearing strata of the Late Cretaceous Horseshoe Canyon Formation and holds numerous specimens from the surrounding Alberta badlands, with over 40 mounted dinosaur skeletons, including specimens of *Tyrannosaurus*, *Albertosaurus*, *Triceratops* and *Stegosaurus* on display in the main dinosaur hall. I was provided with a microscope, their amber collections and a workspace located in one of the main storage areas, behind the scenes. This is where they store the specimens that are not on display and, as with all museums, this actually represents the majority of the collection. It was kind of surreal being surrounded by huge dinosaur fossils, such as *Triceratops* skulls, the likes of which I had never seen before, while the reason for me being there was to examine tiny insects and spiders preserved in fossilized resin from

the same (Cretaceous) time period. Periodically, when I needed a break from the microscope work, I would wander up and down the storage area staring in awe at the remarkable fossils just sitting there in various different states of preparation. During my visit, I was taken out to a dinosaur dig site in the surrounding Badlands, which have yielded most of the fossils in the museum. Whilst at the site I recalled my favourite dinosaur book and the conversation I'd had with my mother three decades earlier. This was a childhood dream come true and I really was quite overwhelmed.

There are several important elements to this story:

- If it was possible for me to end up being a palaeontologist without actually desiring to be one, then there is considerable potential for those who really want to do it.
- You do not need to be an A* pupil at school (though it cannot hurt

and I would advise readers to aim much higher than I did during my early education).
- There is no set road map to becoming a palaeontologist.
- There is a great deal of overlap in terms of the different careers discussed in this book and while you may concentrate on one, e.g. academic research, you may also find yourself being filmed for a TV documentary, talking about fossils to the general public as part of an outreach project, or writing a book.
- Don't underestimate the potential of a lucky break, though you would be ill advised to rely on one.
- Your childhood passion can become a reality (regardless of your age); do not allow others to deter you from your goal.

Now I have my own young children and they too love dinosaurs. I also have a friend with a young daughter who literally eats, sleeps and breathes dinosaurs. Clearly the fascination we have with these remarkable extinct giants (though not all dinosaurs were huge) shows no signs of diminishing, and why should it? I cannot think of anything else that better sparks the imagination of a child. Hence, it was with this in mind that I set about the outline for this book. Of course, there is much more to palaeontology than just dinosaurs, nor is it just a passion for the young. There are plenty of older folk out there who would love to get involved in this fascinating subject.

The important points that I want to get across in this book are that there are no hard and fast rules, in terms of what you can study or research, where you should do it, how you eventually get your foot in the palaeo door, or indeed what age you should be when you start. You can be as young or as old as you like! This is not a book about palaeontology *per se*, so there are no extensive chapters on the history of the science or the diversity of fossils and what they can tell us. There are plenty of other books that cover these subjects. The aim here is to provide some insight into the diverse range of palaeontology jobs that are out there, in addition to what you should consider doing in order to increase your chances of securing one. When I make reference to a website in the text, the full address can be found at the end of the book. My hope is that this book will help some people achieve their palaeontological aspirations and help parents to guide their children's interests.

Dr David Penney FRES, FLS, FRSB, CSci
November 2015

1. What is palaeontology?

The simplest definition is "the study of prehistoric life" and considers several aspects of extinct organisms, such as their identity, origin and evolution, the environment in which they lived, their behaviour and ecology, and what they can tell us about the Earth's past. It became established as a science in the 18th century as a result of Georges Cuvier's work on comparative anatomy, has developed rapidly since and continues to do so. It represents an interface between biology and geology and uses techniques drawn from a wide range of other disciplines, including mathematics, computational sciences, chemistry, materials sciences, physics and engineering. It even contributes to astrobiology, the study of possible extra-terrestrial life on other planets, through developing models of how life may have arisen and by providing techniques for detecting evidence of it.

As our understanding of the history of life on Earth has increased, palaeontology has developed sub-disciplines, permitting further insights into increasingly more specialized elements of the science. These include:

- Invertebrate palaeontology – animals without backbones, such as ammonites, trilobites, echinoderms, molluscs, insects (palaeoentomology) and arachnids (palaeoarachnology).

Ammonites, as an example of invertebrate fossils
(Thomas Bresson, Wikimedia CC-BY-3.0)

- Vertebrate palaeontology – animals with backbones such as non-avian dinosaurs, birds, mammals, fish, reptiles and amphibians (palaeoherpetology).

Fish from the 50 million-year-old Eocene of Wyoming, USA
(Michael Popp, Wikimedia CC0 1.0 Universal Public Domain)

- Palaeobotany – plant fossils, including flowers, leaves, wood and seeds.

Fagus leaf from the 2.6–3.6 million-year-old Pliocene of France
(Didier Descouens, Wikimedia CC BY-SA 4.0)

- Biostratigraphy – the use of fossils to work out the chronological sequence in which rocks were formed. These relative dates can then be converted to absolute dates using radiometric dating.
- Micropalaeontology – microfossils such as mineralized plankton, e.g. diatoms and foraminifera or organic spores and pollen (palynology); often employed by industrial palaeontologists to help locate rock formations that are likely to yield oil.

Microfossils, including radiolarians, sponge spicules and foraminiferans, from marine sediment from the Antarctic continental margin, Eastern Weddell Sea (Hannes Grobe, Wikimedia CC BY-SA 3.0)

- Ichnology – trace fossils, such as footprints, burrows, feeding and egg-laying trace marks, coprolites (fossil faeces), etc. (associating fossilized traces with their makers is often very difficult).
- Taphonomy – the study of what happens from the time an organism dies until the time it becomes a fossil. In addition to direct observation of fossils, researchers may undertake decay experiments on modern organisms.
- Palaeobiology – a more theoretical sub-discipline where fossil data are analysed using quantitative statistical methods or modelling

17

Crustacean burrows from the Middle Jurassic of
Makhtesh Qatan, southern Israel
(Mark A Wilson, Wikimedia Public Domain)

techniques in order to address questions relating to major events in Earth history (e.g. mass extinctions), or to investigate macro-evolutionary patterns and ecological interactions (palaeoecology) over geological timescales.

- Molecular palaeontology – the recovery and analysis of DNA, proteins, carbohydrates and other molecules from ancient animal and plant remains (a relatively young research field that has seen continuous development since the 1950s).
- Palaeogeography – the distribution of organisms over deep time and how geological processes such as plate tectonics resulted in the past and modern day distribution patterns of animals and plants.
- Virtual/computational palaeontology – analysing, interpreting and reconstructing fossil organisms (and their behaviours, e.g. locomotion, including biomechanics and functional morphology) using computers (this is a rapidly developing research field as a result of new technological and computational developments).

In fact, you can take many modern disciplines and add the prefix 'palaeo' in order to develop a more defined sub-discipline of palaeontology. For example, palaeoethology (the study of behaviour in the fossil record), palaeopathology

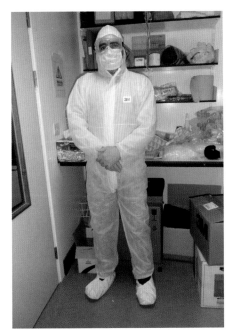

The author in full forensics protective clothing (in order to avoid contamination of samples) prior to entering a dedicated ancient DNA laboratory, during his molecular palaeontology research involving Next Generation Sequencing (left) and running large fossil fish through a CT scanner (right)

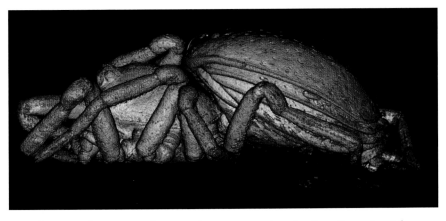

Computed tomography scan reconstructoin of a tiny (1 mm) spider preserved in Eocene Baltic amber – some of my ongoing research (scan and image by Mark Riccio, Cornell University)

Mating insects (froghoppers) from the Jurassic of China, as a combined example of palaeoethology and palaeoentomology (Li et al. 2013, PLoS ONE 8(11): e78188)

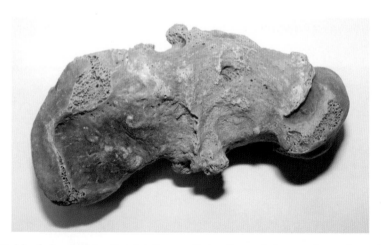

Highly deformed (arthritic) finger digit of an adult cave bear from the Pleistocene of Austria, as an example of palaeopathology

(the study of disease conditions in the fossil record), palaeoentomology (the study of fossil insects), palaeoneurology (the study of endocranial casts/ CT reconstructions to learn about the evolution of brains), palaeogenomics (inferring the presence of particular genes in the fossil record – certain genes code for RNA and proteins specific to particular characteristics, therefore the presence of such character states in the fossil record implies the presence of those genes), to name just a few. Even terms such as palaeoclimatology are in common usage, though given that the study of prehistoric climates may not necessarily involve the direct study of fossil organisms (though sometimes it does), its inclusion as a 'branch' of palaeontology in the strict sense is rather debatable.

Clearly, if you are already an expert in a modern discipline that can potentially be investigated in the fossil record, then you already have many of the prerequisites in order to venture into the palaeo realm. This option may suit professionals looking for a career change whilst still utilizing their existing skills and knowledge. Alternatively, it may form the basis for an advanced research degree, such as a PhD, whether by a young person embarking on it following their undergraduate studies or an older person indulging in their lifelong passion during their retirement. Take a moment to consider your current or previous career (or that of your parents) and pop the 'palaeo' prefix in front of it. Maybe it has potential. It might even represent a new, previously unexplored branch of palaeontology!

2. Why is palaeontology important?

Palaeontology is the study of the history of life on Earth, as documented by the fossil record. Given that humans are a part of that story, it should be of intrinsic interest to us all. However, most people seem more concerned with the present and the future and spend relatively little time considering even their immediate past, let alone what was going on tens or hundreds of millions of years ago. However, the fossil and geological records provide the only source of natural (as opposed to experimental or theoretical) examples of what happens to organisms under conditions the Earth is not experiencing today. Hence, not only is the past the key to the present, but also to the future! Certainly, it can help us shed light on potential significant consequences of abiotic and biotic events occurring today, such as global warming, extinction and biodiversity loss through habitat destruction, overhunting, disease etc. (compared against background extinction rates over deep time). Geologists and palaeontologists appreciate that future situations have probably happened before and that by studying the evidence preserved in the fossil and geological records they have an important role to play in predicting what might happen in the future.

In recent decades the emerging field of molecular biology (or more specifically phylogenomics) has made great advances in understanding the tree of life, mainly as a result of DNA analysis. Unfortunately, DNA does not remain intact indefinitely and so is rarely preserved in the fossil record. Hence, the body fossils studied by traditional palaeontology remain important for understanding how life on Earth evolved and this looks set to remain true regardless of technological advances. If you also consider that more than 99% of all species that have ever existed on Earth are now extinct, then the value of the fossil record for understanding the evolutionary history of life on our planet becomes immediately apparent.

Given the above, and as I hope you will see from the rest of this book, now is an exciting time to be a palaeontologist. It is not a research discipline in decline as some might suggest, but has a significant role to play, both in its own right and as an ever expanding component of large-scale, multidisciplinary research projects of broad global concern.

Geological time spiral of life on Earth – >99% of all species that have ever existed are now extinct (USGS, Wikimedia Public Domain)

23

3. What does a palaeontologist really do?

Depending on where you work, you duties could include any combination of the following:

- Undertaking fieldwork to collect samples and associated data.
- Preparing fossils for scientific research or display purposes.
- Leading and managing volunteers or students on local or overseas field trips.
- Laboratory work, from testing samples to microscopic examination of fossils.
- Engaging in collaborative or individual research projects, with the ultimate aim of writing up and publishing the results in a scientific journal.
- Writing and/or illustrating general interest articles for scientific websites and popular magazines.
- Writing or editing books or invited chapters.
- Peer-reviewing and editing the work of other palaeontologists.
- Writing (or reviewing) grant applications for palaeontological research projects.
- Preparing and delivering lecture courses and hands-on practical classes (this could include the delivery of live interactive videoconferencing presentations as part of online distance learning projects).
- Preparing and presenting talks (and posters) at scientific conferences.
- Developing and managing a website and/or social media presence.
- Recording and classifying samples and curating collections.
- Acquisition and integration of new specimens into existing collections (this may require processing national and international permits and associated documentation).
- Environmental monitoring of display and collections storage areas, along with conservation and restorative work if appropriate.
- Managing displays and exhibitions and providing guided tours for visiting researchers, students and the general public.
- Training and supervising volunteers, new staff and students.
- Developing and maintaining collection databases and records of collection activity, use, and status for annual reports.
- Providing expert advice to a broad range of people, from the general

public to journalists, TV producers, as an expert witness in court, or to a board of directors of an international company.

- Responding to more general inquiries from scientists, governmental and consulting agencies, the public, and others.
- Participating in the activities and development of professional paleontological societies.

Hence, there is a great deal of variation in what you might be expected to do as a palaeontologist and no two days are ever the same. It is far removed from the stereotypical Indiana Jones type job that many people envisage as the life of a typical palaeontologist. Nonetheless, there are often opportunities to undertake fieldwork in remote places and there are also plenty of opportunities for overseas travel to museums or conferences. Life as a palaeontologist has the potential to provide a great combination of travel, fieldwork, teaching, communicating with the public and of course a great deal of personal satisfaction, e.g. as a result of discovering new species or generating new ideas about the history of life on Earth.

The author examining freshly excavated samples at the amber mines in the Dominican Republic, 2006

4. Where do palaeontologists work?

1. Museums

Various different categories of staff are involved with collections care in museums, each with their own role to play. However, these roles often overlap to some degree depending on the museum in question. A useful source of information regarding careers in museums is the Museums Association website.

i)   Curator

Essentially, a museum curator is responsible for the day-to-day care and management of a collection of specimens and its associated data, which may be digital (e.g. databases) and/or physical (e.g. correspondence archives). A key goal of this role is to inform, educate and inspire the public, through the construction of innovative and creative exhibitions that appeal to a wide cross-section of the population. It can be a varied job and often includes other activities, such as public relations, marketing, budget and staff management, fundraising and educational outreach programmes. The specific responsibilities vary from museum to museum. At a small independent museum, a curator may have more of a managerial role. This would involve looking after the collection, operations, staff and volunteers. By contrast, at a large national or university museum, a curator may be responsible for one specific area of the collection, for research in a specific field of knowledge and for the management of a small team of staff and volunteers.

In many museums there currently seems to be a shift away from specialist academic research activities (by curators) to a more general curatorial role. In some museums, previously separate departments (each with their own curators) have been merged under the care of just a single curator in order to cut costs and save money. For example, I am aware of an instance of a Mineralogy Department and a Palaeontology Department being merged under the umbrella of Earth Sciences, with the loss of one of the curatorial roles (and of course the loss of expert knowledge). Research on the collections still happens, but this is normally conducted by visiting researchers, supported by the curatorial staff.

This situation is also reflected in the qualifications required for application to many curatorial jobs currently on offer. Previously, such positions would

Tylers Museum fossil room display and storage cabinets
(Tylers Museum, Wikimedia CC BY-SA 3.0 NL)

have required a PhD and a substantial list of research publications, but nowadays such a high level of education is not normally required. So, if it is a research career you are looking for this might not be the right choice for you. However, if you adore fossils and wish to be surrounded by thousands (if not millions) of remarkable specimens on a daily basis, that you can get hands-on with, then maybe it is. Most palaeontology curatorial positions will require a Master's degree (sometimes a PhD) in museum studies, palaeontology, geology, systematics or a related discipline. Sometimes an appropriate undergraduate degree plus several years of experience working with museum collections in a position with similar responsibilities to those of the job being applied for may also suffice. Note how 'museum studies' is listed first. This is because there seems to be an increasing importance being placed on the professional context of such roles. In rare cases you will still see job adverts for curatorial roles in palaeontology without any museological qualifications included as part of the person specification, but these are few and far between these days. In many cases, it is possible to gain professional museology qualifications whilst on the job, but obviously if you can bring this to the table in your initial application (in addition to specialist palaeontological skills), it will certainly be looked on favourably. Some universities run undergraduate courses on museum studies, or you could embark on a one-year Masters course following a degree in a different discipline. There are also various online course providers who offer professional online continuing education in museum studies topics leading to professional credentials, but without the travel and subsistence costs associated with attending a university.

Curatorial positions also require demonstrable experience of working in a museum and an understanding of issues relating to care and management of collections, such as optimum environmental parameters for best storage practice and preventative conservation. Indeed, many applications require you write a 'statement of collection management philosophy', or something similar. Likewise, an excellent knowledge of relational databases for collections management and web-based applications for outreach work are also required skills. So, if you think this would be your chosen career then it is a really good idea to start volunteering in a museum at your earliest opportunity. Obviously, specialist knowledge of the taxonomy and identification of a group of fossils is also highly desirable. However, this can be rather hit or miss, given that different museums can have different collections priorities and strengths, both taxonomically and regionally, or with regard to the particular position on offer.

ii)   Researcher

These days many of the smaller, regional museums are reducing (or even totally ceasing) their research activities in favour of a more public outreach and education approach. The main reason for this seems to be the new breed of non-academic directors being required to make significant budget cuts. They tend to see research as an expendable luxury that does not contribute to the perceived main function of the museum as a public entity, i.e. providing exhibits and public programs. However, significant research agendas still persist in many of the larger national museums, which hold some of the most important collections. As a result, museum research tends to be more collections based and systematic in nature, and many have access to excellent preparation facilities and the latest cutting edge technology, either in-house or through affiliated universities or other research institutes. Research opportunities may be at post-graduate level, leading to a higher degree or may be post-doctoral research positions on a specific project. These days you are unlikely to see a vacancy that does not call for expertise in a specified area of research, so it can be rather hit and miss trying to find a vacancy that matches your specific skill sets. Nonetheless, sometimes the specifics are rather open-ended. In such circumstances, the better that your knowledge, experience and taxonomic expertise match the strengths of the collections (or the interests of the current curator in charge), then the greater your chances of being selected for interview.

iii)   Technician/Preparator

Some of the larger museums with very active palaeontology research programs or exhibits will have their own staff of dedicated technicians to assist in the various projects. Obviously, the requirements of a particular appointment will be dependent on the type of research being undertaken, but essentially you could find yourself in charge of a large, multi-purpose palaeontological preparation facility employing a range of skills from thin section preparation, acid maceration, polishing amber, through to extracting bones from their rock matrix and making full skeletal reconstructions. You may also need to be able to develop supporting mounts and armatures for storage and display of the fossils. In some cases you will need to be skilled in the use of a range of specialist equipment, such as scanning electron microscopes and computed tomography (CT) scanners, etc.

There are currently no formal degrees or training programs in fossil preparation. Most fossil preparators acquire their skills and abilities through a combination of academic study and practical training; experience is an essential component in developing the necessary skill sets. A good preparator needs great patience, focus and attention to detail. Preparing even a single small fossil can take many days of work and poor preparation techniques can potentially ruin a very important research or display specimen. The best way to determine if you are suited to preparation is to volunteer in an established fossil preparation lab. These can be found in some museums and universities, but there are also independent preparators who prepare fossils for the retail trade. Increasingly, these days, some private fossil collectors are getting much more skilled at preparing their own finds and it may be possible to make contact with such people via local societies and meetings in order to get some initial training. This approach can be useful for building up an initial 'portfolio' of projects that may help demonstrate your manual dexterity and facilitate easier access to larger prep labs and also to highlight your potential suitability for future job appointments.

An undergraduate degree or equivalent in geology with an emphasis on pal-aeontology (anatomy and taxonomy) is the usual basic minimum require-ment (though a Masters degree would be preferable). However, this does not count for much without a considerable amount of relevant practical

Barosaurus full skeletal mount on display at the American Museum of Natural History (Greg, Wikimedia CC BY 2.0)

Royal Tyrrell Museum of Palaeontology preparation laboratory
(Prakashsubbarao, Wikimedia Public Domain)

experience, through which you can demonstrate your specialist technical skills. A fundamental knowledge of stratigraphy, sedimentology, comparative anatomy and evolution are also desirable. Given the lack of a dedicated training syllabus for this job, the more practical experience you have the better are your chances of getting selected for interview. This can include field and laboratory work, including excavating, consolidating, collecting and documenting new fossil discoveries; experience using manual and mechanical fossil preparation techniques, including use of rock saws, air scribes, air abrasives, acid maceration techniques, etc., molding, casting, restoration, and conservation of fossils. A good working knowledge of how new technologies are being applied to palaeontology is also advantageous. For example, these days 3D digital scanning and printing is revolutionizing how skeletal reconstructions (for research as well as display) are compiled faster than ever before. It has the particular advantage of allowing the generation of symmetrical reconstructions when just a partial fossil is available.

iv)   Conservator

Once we have found and prepared our fossils it is important that this palaeontological information be preserved for future generations through proper conservation and storage. Given that many fossils are millions (if not tens or hundreds of millions) of years old it is not unreasonable to expect that they are all highly resilient to degradation. However, this is not true. For example, as soon as you remove amber from its rock matrix and expose it to air and light it starts to oxidize. This can lead to darkening of the fossil resin and eventually to the formation of a thick crust over its surface. In the worst case scenario the specimen will disintegrate completely. The process can be exacerbated by storing amber specimens under inappropriate environmental conditions, such as exposed to light and high fluctuations of temperature and humidity.

Another example concerns fossils from the famous oil shale pit deposits of Messel, Germany, formed during the Eocene (ca. 47 million years ago). This Lagerstätte preserves a diverse assemblage of organisms with remarkable clarity and structural integrity, due to the unique depositional characteristics of the original lake. The oil shale contains around 40% water. When a slab is removed from the surrounding rock, it soon dries out, cracks, and can transform to a pile of rubble in a few hours, destroying any fossils with it. The fossils are conserved by first preparing them on one side, which is then covered with artificial resin. After the new substrate hardens, the other side of the fossil is prepared. This technique is called the artificial resin transfer method.

Yet another example relates to the pyrite permineralization preservation of the Early Eocene (Ypresian) plant fossils of the London Clay Formation, UK. Unfortunately, the benefits of this type of preservation for 3D morphological reconstructions and tissue and cellular studies, are offset by the ease with which pyrite breaks down in humid, oxygenated conditions. Some of the most important fossils (held in the Natural History Museum, London) are now housed in silicon oil to retard further decay.

There are of course many more examples. Larger museums usually have a dedicated Conservation Department (though many have been reduced in size significantly due to budget cuts in recent years), which deals with the entire range of specimens held in the collections, including monitoring the environmental conditions under which they are stored and displayed.

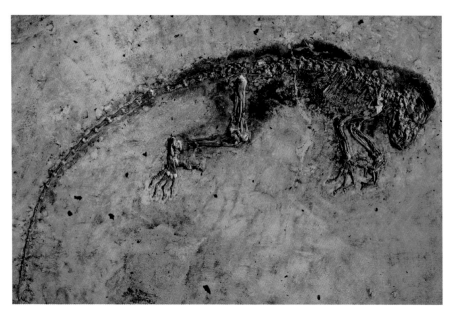

Fossil primate from the Eocene oil shale of Messel, Germany,
prepared using the resin transfer technique
(Franzen et al. 2009, PLoS ONE 4(5): e5723)

Conservators aim to minimize deterioration but also need to be skilled in the art of restoring specimens when required, in order to give them a new lease of life while retaining their scientific integrity. In many cases conservators are self-employed specialists and work on a freelance basis. Most conservators are graduates, with post-graduate conservation training considered vital if you do not have a first degree in conservation. A good knowledge of chemistry is very useful. For more information visit the web pages of the UK Institute for Conservation, which runs an accreditation scheme for freelance conservators.

v)   Educator

Most of the larger museums have an Education Department. Science educators help develop and deliver educational activities within the museum. These may include individual school workshops, educational tours, camp-ins, public programs, lecture presentations, and community outreach and events programming. Such programs tend to reflect the mandate and strengths of

Large ammonites provide great hands-on opportunities for children in museum education settings

the institution, whilst also meeting the needs of the relevant educational curriculum. So, unless the museum is dedicated solely to palaeontology, you are unlikely to spend too much time getting hands-on with fossils. Also, because the specimens are being constantly handled by children, they are not going to be important or significant fossils from the main collection. Most Education Departments have their own teaching collections, which usually consist of rather common fossils that can be easily replaced if damaged or lost. The educational wing of the Royal Tyrrell Museum of Palaeontology in Alberta has its own fully equipped broadcast-style Distance Learning Studio. The educators are able to present live, interactive, media-rich videoconferencing programs to schools and the public throughout Alberta, across North America, and overseas.

A good degree in science or education should suffice as an entry-level qualification. Experience of working with children in a learning environment would also be a useful advantage. For online distance learning you will need additional computer literacy and audiovisual skills, such as proficiency in using cameras, microphones, mixers, etc.

vi)   Volunteer

Volunteers do important work in museums, from leading guided gallery tours to helping to catalog the collections behind the scenes. This is true of all museums, not just the large nationals. In the current economic climate, which has seen many paid museum positions lost, some institutions would find it difficult to conduct their full range of activities effectively without their volunteer force. Museum volunteers range in age from school students up to those in retirement. If you are studying at university it is well worth your while to make a few hours available each week in order to do voluntary work in a museum. It is best if you can do the same time and day each week and you must be able to commit to any position offered, otherwise it will be a waste of time for all involved, including the curator in charge who may then think twice about offering such positions in the future. The knowledge, transferable and practical skills you gain will be extremely useful and can be used as relevant hands-on experience in future applications for jobs, research grants, etc. or may even form the basis for your final year undergraduate project. Such environments also present potentially useful networking opportunities, as you never know who may be visiting to research the collections. If you have more time available then you may also be able to undertake your own collections-based research projects.

2. Universities
      i)   Researcher
     ii)   Lecturer

These two roles often go hand in hand, with lecturers doing some research and researchers doing some lecturing. Both normally require a PhD qualification in order to be a full time member of staff. More often than not an early stage worker will start as a post-doctoral researcher, usually funded by an external research grant, and then they may be taken on as a permanent member of staff once the grant has ended … but this is by no means always the case and many post-doctoral researchers find themselves with periods of unemployment between grants. This situation is far from ideal, and often a researcher needs to start applying for new grants well before their current grant has come to an end. Competition for grants is intense, so this can be a stressful and disappointing process, but it can also be very satisfying when a large grant secures your future for the next few years.

In the UK, getting a PhD normally requires:

- An undergraduate degree, which takes three to four years (very rarely a student can go straight to a higher degree without an undergraduate qualification if their background experience is appropriate, though they do this at the expense of a broad education base that may benefit them further down the line). Appropriate subjects that lead on to palaeontology include zoology (or botany for those wishing to study palaeobotany) and geology, with some universities offering joint biology/geology courses.
- A Masters degree, which takes one to two years (sometimes this is not necessary, although a Masters by research provides excellent experience of doing a large research project and preparing a thesis, not gained in an undergraduate course). Some Masters palaeobiology courses also fill in substantial information gaps for students coming from biology degrees, or from more distant disciplines.
- A PhD, which takes three to five years (longer if done part-time).
- Following the PhD, most people typically have one to five post-doctoral research positions, each of one to three years duration, before securing a full-time permanent position, usually as a lecturer. It is also seen as preferable if at least one of the post-doc positions is taken in a research institute overseas.

A permanent position in academia can be extremely rewarding. However, reaching this point following the above outline is not as simple as it sounds. You will need to be prepared for, and able to manage, uncertainty, instability and a rather poor work–life balance during the early stages. It is also worth noting that in recent decades there has been a distinct shift from curiosity driven research (enjoyed by many palaeontologists in the past) to more thematic, interdisciplinary studies which address issues of current concern and hence are more likely to secure research grants and result in publications in high impact academic journals, which reflect better on the host institution. In real terms what this means is that it is not always possible to study your primary interest; you need to focus on what is considered scientifically and socio-economically 'sexy' at the time.

iii)   Technician

University technicians have varied roles. Much of the work involves main-taining research laboratories, curating teaching collections and other materials and preparing specimens and laboratories for practical classes. They may also be skilled at operating specialist equipment and may be required to participate in residential field courses. The palaeontological element of this role really depends heavily on how much palaeontology teaching/research occurs at the university concerned. At some places there may be a substantial amount (more likely in universities that run a palaeobiology Masters degree course), whereas at others there may be barely any. There is little scope for personal research as a technician. Trainee technicians can usually start with a good set of GCSE level qualifications, but higher grades usually require additional qualifications, such as A-levels, a degree or equivalent professional qualifications. There is often scope for on-the-job education, such as attending college one day per week to gain professional qualifications.

iv)   Honorary positions

Most university departments have honorary research positions available under various different titles, such as Visiting Scientist, Affiliated Researcher, Honorary Lecturer, etc. These are unpaid positions, with the university benefitting from having their address on any resulting papers published by the researcher, who benefits in turn from access to laboratory and library facilities (usually including remote access to digital content which is extremely useful). It also provides the researcher with a formal academic address, which can be necessary in order to acquire loans of fossils from museums and other research institutions. This is often useful for unemployed researchers between post-doctoral appointments, for retired individuals or for those who want a university affiliation but without all the additional commitment that comes with full-time employment.

There are many personal benefits to having an honorary position. You are usually able to follow your own curiosity driven research agenda, rather than being required to research specific topics that are currently considered en vogue (and more likely to attract research grants). Furthermore, as a formally employed member of staff progresses up the career ladder, their administrative and teaching duties also increase considerably, more often than not at the expense of their own personal research. Indeed, senior colleagues I have discussed this with have told me that they no longer do any research at all because they spend most of their time trying to obtain funding so that their research staff can do it. Clearly, this change of responsibilities and duties suits some people, but it is certainly not for everybody.

The best way to get such a position is to contact an academic member of staff in the relevant department, preferably one whose research program most closely reflects your own interests. However, remember that by doing so out of the blue, you are adding to their administrative duties as highlighted above! Hence, a short, succinct and polite approach is the way forward. It is a good idea to mention your research background, achievements and what it is you would like to do, along with attaching a brief curriculum vitae. There is normally a rather informal application process, which needs to be reviewed by a committee before such positions are awarded. In the past such positions were often open-ended, but these days they are usually awarded for a period of one to three years. So, if you are offered one, make sure you make sufficient use of it in order to justify its renewal!

3. Geoconservation Parks

Palaeontological resources include considerably more than the fossils that intrigue us so much. They also include the background data in terms of the context in which the fossils are preserved. There is an increasing trend towards preserving these features as National Parks, or more specifically as Geoparks. In November 2015, the 195 Member States of UNESCO ratified the creation of the new label: UNESCO Global Geoparks, expressing governmental recognition of the importance of managing outstanding geological sites and landscapes in a holistic manner. The Geopark concept can be applied worldwide, but can be especially important in the developing world. Integrating the preservation of geological heritage into strategies for sustainable economic development can promote sustainable tourism (alongside associated additional economic and cultural activities), leading to job creation in local rural communities, for the benefit of those communities.

Some fossil yielding localities are also classified as World Heritage Sites. They are listed by the United Nations Educational, Scientific and Cultural Organization (UNESCO) as being of special cultural or physical significance. From an Earth sciences perspective, a site can be awarded WHS designation if it is an outstanding example representing major stages of Earth's history, including the record of life, significant on-going geological processes in the development of landforms, or significant geomorphic or physiographic features. Palaeontological examples include: Australian Fossil Mammal Sites (Riversleigh/Naracoorte); Dinosaur Provincial Park, Canada; Chengjiang Fossil Site, China; the Jurassic Coast of Dorset, UK; and the Messel Pit Fossil Site, Germany to name just a few.

The famous Jurassic coast of Dorset, UK

You can find more information, including a full list of sites and an employment and internships link, on the World Heritage Convention website. Of course, it is also worth visiting the home pages of the individual sites for voluntary and paid employment opportunities. Also keep an eye out for festivals, open days and other events associated with these (and similar) sites. For example, there is an annual (May) Fossil Festival held in Lyme Regis, Dorset, where it is possible for the entire family to get involved in all sorts of different palaeo-related activities. A similar event (September) has also been run in Scarborough since 2014.

4. Industry

The primary requirement within oil and gas work relating to palaeontology is for biostratigraphers (palynologists, micropalaeontologists and nannopalaeontologists). These enable tight correlation of strata by identification of the species and variants within cuttings samples. Despite the eco-concerns associated with these fuels, they look set to remain the major energy source for the coming decades.

There is fun for the whole family at fossil festivals,
such as this one held in Scarborough, 2015

Biostratigraphic palaeontologists used to be essential to the business of finding and producing fossil fuels, such as oil and gas. However, advances in seismic imaging of the subsurface, reservoir modelling, chemostratigraphy and paleomagnetism have diminished the role of the micropalaeontologist somewhat. Nowadays, companies typically recruit more generalized geologists, who have preferentially studied palaeontology (principally biostratigraphy). Nonetheless, biostratigraphic analyses still need to be done and this requires palaeo expertise. In offshore situations there will be both consultant biostratigraphers and geologists and both report to the in-house geology/biostrat team who then make the relevant decisions. Onshore, a geologist will work to outsource the analyses to independent consultancies and integrate and analyze the data afterwards. Some oil companies may hire a biostratigrapher for this role. Students specializing in stratigraphic palaeontology are in short supply and some companies provide contract work for graduate students as encouragement toward future employment with their company. There are also several universities that run biostratigraphy Masters degrees.

Most industrial palaeontologists working in these fields tend to stay within their area of specialty where there is limited scope for progression within the company ranks. Palaeontologists who demonstrate skills in planning and leadership are able to move up the ladder within corporate organizations but must usually leave palaeontology in order to do so. Industrial palaeontologists are not at the top of the high-demand list but tend to be in short supply.

Industry jobs are also expanding in the field of environmental consulting. Countries around the world are passing more restrictive laws regarding the collection and preservation of fossils. This means that industrial infrastructure, such as new roads, major pipelines, electric and phone cables, as well as natural gas and oil drilling need palaeontologists to survey and salvage fossils collected during the construction projects. These jobs are typically undertaken by environmental consultancy agencies, which need people trained in the collection and preparation of fossils. A Masters degree in geology or biology, with appropriate field experience in palaeontology, is normally required.

5. Media and Arts
There seems to be constant media interest in the origins of life on Earth, dinosaurs, new fossil discoveries documenting the oldest this or the oldest that, etc. Consequently, there are ample opportunities for those with a palaeontological bent, whether as a science journalist, a television presenter/

Palaeoartist Richard Bizley (www.Bizleyart.com) with his paintings of fossil insect scenes from the major geological time periods, at the Lyme Regis fossil festival, 2012

researcher, an online blogger or as a specialist palaeoartist/model maker. Having the skill of being able to communicate new scientific discoveries to a broad lay audience in an interesting and informative manner will always be in demand. You will need to be able to talk science to scientists, understand the science (though many researchers seem to get away without these two skills) and then be able to communicate that science accurately to those without a science background.

Such stories also need to be illustrated, whether it by still images, model replicas or special effects involving computer generated imagery and those skilled in these techniques will also be in high demand. This is particularly true of those with unusual, combined skill sets including palaeontological expertise alongside a more pragmatic artistic or technical skill. Of course, you can set your sights on such a career from the outset and develop the necessary skills independently, but you may find yourself in a rather

Palaeoartistic reconstruction of a pachycephalosaurid dinosaur used in a scientific publication describing palaeopathologies related to head-butting (Peterson et al. 2013, PLoS ONE 8(7): e68620)

specialized niche. This may work just fine, but remember also that the more niche-dependent and specialized an organism is, the greater is the chance that it might go extinct!

There are often opportunities for freelance consultants and researchers in the multi-billion dollar movie industry (take *Jurassic Park* and its spin offs as prime examples), where the facts and creatures portrayed need to be as true to life as possible (albeit with some artistic license). Hence, palaeontologists with a good working knowledge of functional morphology are often consulted during film production in order to make sure the extinct organisms being depicted are moving in an appropriate manner. Similarly, there is not much point having a dinosaur in a movie that is totally out of context of the environment in which it was presumed to have lived. Hence, palaeoecologists will need to be consulted in order to comment on what other animals and plants may have been present and how they may have interacted, in addition to the climate setting, etc. Outside of the film industry, household broadcasters also have a requirement for such expertise. For example, the BBC has its own dedicated Natural History Unit.

6. The Independent Palaeontologist

Gone are the days when you had to be working in a museum or university in order to gain access to all the resources required to conduct effective palaeontological research. There is an incredible wealth of information freely available online, ranging from large taxonomic and palaeo/biogeographic databases (though the accuracy of the data contained in many of these has recently been questioned, with concerns that more than 50% of entries may be based on misidentifications!), identification resources, statistical software and graphical/illustration packages, daily digests of the latest cutting edge palaeontology research direct to your social media news feeds, and academic journals. Some of the journals are freely available (Open Access), but others have the full content hidden behind rather expensive paywalls.

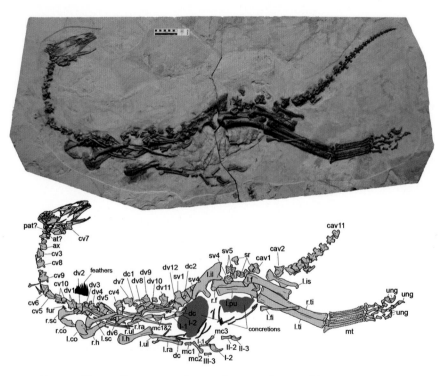

Free online software can be used to produce publication quality illustrations similar to the above therizinosaur dinosaur from the Cretaceous of China (Pu et al. 2013, PLoS ONE 8(5): e63423)

However, more often than not, if you email the author of the paper they will usually be happy to send you a pdf copy of their paper for personal research use. Even the very rare older literature is now freely available online via the Biodiversity Heritage Library website and this is constantly expanding its content. So, in essence, it is often possible to conduct research in certain areas of palaeontology that is equivalent to that of paid academics, but from the comfort of your own home. You can even publish it in the same journals! A note of warning here though, writing scientific papers properly is something that takes a considerable degree of practice. Before you submit your first paper it is a very good idea to have your manuscript critically appraised by somebody who is experienced in publishing in academic journals. This may prevent the shock and disappointment of a harsh rejection letter from the journal editor! Also, make sure you select an appropriate journal for your topic and check for page charges beforehand because some require you pay rather large amounts per page in order to publish your paper (this is especially true of the so-called 'predatory journals', which are on the increase and should be avoided).

Indeed, many professionals at various institutions recognize the potential opportunities this presents as a resource for collaborative research ventures. Big questions often require big data! In many cases collecting such data are beyond the means of an individual research team and it is not uncommon these days for researchers to engage the public for assistance with data collection. This approach of incorporating scientific activities conducted by non-professional scientists is often referred to as citizen science, public participation in scientific research, crowd science, civic science, volunteer science, community-based research, etc. Anyone can be a citizen scientist and such involvement is becoming increasingly popular. Some projects have been remarkably successful in advancing scientific knowledge, and most also strive to help participants learn about the organisms they are observing and to experience how scientific investigations are conducted.

It is also relatively easy and cheap to set yourself up with an informative online and social media presence. However, remember that it is important that you very carefully consider anything that you put online, because once it is there it can be very difficult to erase completely. Whatever you post can be read by just about anybody, including potential future collaborators or even employers! So, just a few words of caution in this regard: while the internet can be an extremely useful tool for promoting your self interests, it can also serve to cause potential problems if used with reckless abandon!

Fossils for sale at the Bakewell Rock Exchange, 2015

Of course, you will also need access to fossils on which to work. Established scientists are often (but not always!) able to secure specific specimens on loan from museums. Sometimes the museum will not send specimens out and the researcher will need to arrange to visit the museum in person. In very rare circumstances specimens are unavailable for research purposes for various (sometimes idiosyncratic) reasons. Most local museums have a volunteer program, so it is usually possible to get access to at least some of the collections. You will normally need to do something in return for this access, such as help the curator update and manage the collections, but this is all good experience and a great way to learn and develop your skills. Another benefit of museums is that they often have copies of otherwise very difficult to obtain specialist books and scientific journals. In addition, these days many museums are digitizing their collections and making the images of their specimens and the associated data freely available online. In some cases the images may be rather simple and not particularly suitable for certain research purposes, but in others the projects are extremely ambitious, with some institutions aiming to provide rotatable 3D images of all their specimens (such projects can take many years ... and are also a good opportunity for voluntary experience). Of course, these data alone can be useful as a research database. Becoming affiliated with a university via an honorary appointment (as discussed earlier) will potentially open the doors of museums further afield, including overseas, for research visits and loan of specimens.

You can always go out and collect your own fossils and this is a great way to make sure that you have the exact provenance and all the associated data that you need for whatever it is you have in mind. It can also be the most satisfying way of obtaining your material, especially if you find something very rare or remarkable. Finally, you can purchase fossils for your research, either at fossil shows or online, but in these situations you need to be wary of fake specimens and the correct provenance of such specimens is often difficult to determine, which can reduce their scientific value drastically. Nonetheless, there are reputable dealers out there and it is not unheard of to find undescribed fossil species in the marketplace! Indeed, I have come across several specimens that I immediately identified as something new in various seller outlets, physical and online. It is often the case that sellers will donate such specimens to museums in order that they can be formally described and made available to future researchers. I have even been contacted by wealthy individuals who are on the lookout for such specimens, so that they can purchase them for donation to museums!

Subfossil stingless bee in Colombian copal obtained from a commerical dealer and representing a new species that I described and named after my daughter Amelia in 2013. This specimen is now held in the collections of the Natural History Museum, London

Dean Lomax (deanrlomax.co.uk) with his certificate and gold medal for winning the first prize at the Set for Britain science communication event held at the House of Commons, London, 2015

Regardless of how you come across your fossils you need to follow local health and safety guidelines and also be aware of local laws and international legislation with regard to the removal of fossils from particular localities. These can vary from site to site and from country to country. Such considerations do need to be taken seriously because it is not that uncommon these days to hear of palaeontologists being arrested and fined or even imprisoned for fossil related offences!

Finally, do not underestimate the potential and resourcefulness of the independent palaeontologist. It is not just an option for those who do not have the grades to get on a university course. For some, it is a pre-determined career choice! Of course, there are pros and cons. You generally have the potential to gain better background and specialist knowledge via going to university and in theory the qualifications should help open doors later, but it is possible to get more hands-on practical experience by just getting stuck in and learning the theory as you go along. An excellent example of the latter approach is the young Doncaster-based palaeontologist Dean Lomax, who has an excellent range of accomplishments under his belt. These include numerous research papers in academic journals, a highly acclaimed (by professional palaeontologists) book on *Dinosaurs of the British Isles*, and a prime-time two-part television documentary on the same topic. In addition, he won the Mendel Gold Medal as first prize for presenting the results of scientific research at the Set for Britain 2015 competition held at the House of Commons, London (where he was competing against post-doctoral researchers from the likes of Cambridge and Oxford) and he was presented with the Marsh Palaeontology Award 2015 at the Natural History Museum, London, which recognizes UK-based (groups or individuals) who have made a significant contribution to palaeontology.

7. The Fossil Trade

Of course, there is potential for making vast sums of money through selling exceptionally rare, high-end fossils, but people who actually have the means to do this are few and far between. Besides, such practices are often frowned upon by academics and most of the general public, who would prefer to see such important fossils accessioned into museum collections so that they can be made available for research purposes and for public display. The trade of high-end fossils, such as complete dinosaurs and other vertebrates, is under ever increasing scrutiny, and many governments are banning the export of these fossils. Nonetheless, the huge sums that such fossils can potentially sell for to extremely wealthy private collectors, in conjunction with the often rather minor sentences (e.g. three months in jail) or small fines handed down for the breach of pertinent laws, are fuelling a black market fossil smuggling trade. This is not a good thing and not something you should consider doing! It is still possible to see complete dinosaur skeletons for sale via some of the large auction houses, but it is equally common to see news headlines concerning convictions related to fossil smuggling. In many cases the fossils seized are repatriated to their country of origin.

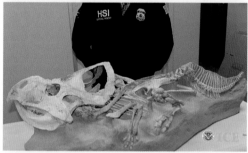

Fossils illegally imported into the US from Asia, seized by US
Immigration and Customs Enforcement (ICE) officials
(photos courtesy of ICE, Public Domain)

In reality, there are very few people who are able to make a comfortable living out of selling fossils. It can often be impossible to recover the financial and time costs of collecting and preparing just a single specimen. Most people who sell fossils tend to do so as an addition to their normal day-to-day job, and the money they make is usually used to purchase new specimens that they have no intention of selling and that they would otherwise be unable to afford. In many cases, people get into selling fossils when their own private collection becomes too large and they need to downsize it in order to make

*An example of fossils for sale at a large trade fair in Munich, 2015
(photo courtesy of John Nudds)*

room for new material. This may result from field collection of numerous common fossils whilst searching for a particularly elusive specimen. Even under these circumstances many collectors would be reluctant to sell their specimens and prefer to just give them away, exchange them with other collectors, or just hoard them.

Nonetheless, there are those who do manage to make the fossil trade a full time, legitimate career choice. They may run a dedicated fossil shop (usually in a tourist area associated with fossils) or may ply their trade online. In tourist areas, the owners are able to supplement their income by leading guided fossil tours. Some of the dealers collect their own fossils, but there are also wholesalers who stock a diverse range of material from further afield. There are also major international fossil fairs (e.g. Tucson, Munich, Stuttgart, Alsace, etc.) where bona fide dealers can purchase new stock at trade prices. It is worth noting that there are lots of fake fossils out there (particularly notable in this regard are some fossils [especially trilobites] from Morocco), so it is important to know how to differentiate these from the genuine article.

Fake Moroccan Dicranurus trilobite clones entirely made of resin, but set in legitimate Devonian matrix. If they are sold as replicas it is not a problem, but often they are not and there is always the potential that such specimens can enter the market as 'legitimate' fossils (photo fossilmuseum.net)

Pete Lawrance (who runs www.bigfossil.com) with a copy of his book: Trilobites of the World: An atlas of 1000 photographs. Pete has been in the fossil trade for 34 years, after 8 years as a museum palaeontologist

Many fossil dealers have excellent expert knowledge of specific groups that interest them, but also of fossils in general. Just consider how many different fossils pass through their hands compared to those of an academic research scientist who may spend an entire year studying just a single fossil! Of course, this is not true of all fossil dealers, some have more of a passion for palaeontology than others. As already highlighted, there is potential for overlap in most palaeontological career realms and I have co-authored research papers with fossil shop owners in the past! Some also write their own books which are well received by academics and amateurs alike.

8. Palaeontology as a Hobby

Many people collect and study fossils as amateurs, and of course, this was the predecessor of modern palaeontology. Professionals and amateurs alike collect fossils for their scientific value, their beauty, their intrigue, or to sell or exchange. There are some professional palaeontologists who frown on fossil collectors and who are of the opinion that all fossils belong in museums. Nonetheless, there are probably more professional palaeontologists who reached their positions, in part, because they developed their interest and honed their knowledge and skills as a result of collecting fossils themselves when they were younger.

As I experienced, and as I know to be true of others, a child's passion and thirst for knowledge about a particular subject cannot be satisfied without the hands-on experience of personal discovery. Furthermore, some of the most important discoveries in the history of palaeontology have been made by collectors or explorers, who would not be classed as professional palaeontologists. This still holds true for recent discoveries. For example, see the extensive literature on Mary Anning (1799–1847), who became famous worldwide for her important finds in the Jurassic marine fossil beds in the cliffs along the English Channel at Lyme Regis, Southwest England. Her finds included the first ichthyosaur skeleton correctly identified; the first two plesiosaur skeletons; the first pterosaur skeleton discovered outside of Germany; important fossil fishes ... and more. In more recent times, the explorer Sue Hendrickson discovered the largest, most extensive and best preserved *Tyrannosaurus rex* specimen ever found (in the summer of 1990), which is now on permanent display at the Field Museum of Natural History in Chicago (I was fortunate enough to have seen this magnificent specimen when I gave a lecture at the museum back in 1998). Back on this side of the pond, in 2015 two brothers, Nick and Rob Hanigan, found the first skeleton of a carnivorous dinosaur from the Jurassic of Wales. They donated

Sue, the most complete fossil skeleton of a Tyrannosaurus rex specimen ever found (Connie Ma, Wikimedia CC BY-SA 2.0)

this important find to the National Museums Wales, in Cardiff, where it is currently on display to the public and the subject of scientific research.

Nonetheless, there are ethical concerns with regard to science and geo/conservation in general. Anybody wishing to collect fossils should familiarize themselves with such issues in addition to any legal restrictions or collecting permits that may be required. Check to see if there is a general or site-specific collecting code. Also be aware of the relevant health and safety aspects of collecting in potentially hazardous areas such as quarries and beneath cliffs, where you may be subject to rock falls or being cut off by incoming tides.

Regardless of where you live there is bound to be at least one reasonably accessible fossil-rich locality where you can get started (see useful websites and further information). Try and select a site for which a reliable field guide is available, in order to help you interpret and classify your finds most accurately. If you are lucky you may be able to find a free app to help identify your fossils. For example, the University of Kansas, with support from the National Science Foundation, has developed an app called *The Digital Atlas of Ancient Life* (available for free on iTunes) that will enable anyone with an iPhone or iPad to identify their fossil finds. The app links to pictures, maps and information about the age of the fossils. It focuses on fossils from Kansas and the US Midwest, but with the increased digitization of museum collections worldwide, it should not be too long before similar resources become available for other regions (an open access description of this app project can be seen here: http://palaeo-electronica.org/content/2015/1269-commentary-digital-atlas-of-ancient-life). An ongoing project at the Natural History Museum, London aims to digitize more than 350 named species of plant fossils from the Early Eocene (Ypresian) London Clay Formation, UK. Furthermore, this project will present 3D reconstruction data derived from computed tomography scanning, which will allow 3D rotation and digital dissection of the specimens by anybody with an internet connection and the appropriate software. Rock and fossil fairs are also a great opportunity to acquire fossils from further afield and to share your passion and learn from like-minded individuals.

If fieldwork does not appeal to you or is impractical then it is worth investigating the palaeontological strengths of your local museum collections. You will need to find out what they have behind the scenes rather than just on display. There are many advantages to this approach. You can formulate your initial learning and research goals based on what is readily available to you (assuming you can get access to the material) and this also has the potential to be of direct benefit to the museum. If you are really lucky, the curator may have special expertise in that element of the collection and might be willing to serve as an informal mentor, with the potential for co-authored scientific publications as a result! Alternatively, you can try the open-minded option and contact the relevant curator stating your interest in fossils and asking if there is anything you can do to help. The only problem with this approach is that you might come across as not having any particular interest or in not having done any relevant background research about the collections concerned.

Just as with professional researchers, you may decide to concentrate on the total fossil diversity of one particular deposit or you may opt to focus on a particular group of organisms from a single locality or from a range of different localities and time periods. Such a formulated approach can lead to the accumulation of significant expert knowledge in a relatively short period of time and who knows where that might lead in terms of future employment? There are no hard and fast rules!

5. Concluding remarks

In summary, to become an effective palaeontologist, it is desirable for a person to possess the following key skills and attributes:

- An interest and broad knowledge of the natural world (both physical and biological).
- Good observational skills and attention to detail.
- An ability to work independently and as part of a team.
- A logical and methodological approach to work.
- Good creative thought processes and the ability to critically appraise existing ideas.
- Good communications skills (spoken and written) and a friendly disposition.
- If fieldwork is required (not all palaeontologists do it) you will need a decent level of general fitness and a willingness to travel and be away from home for (potentially) long periods of time.

In addition, specialist knowledge and research skills allow greater potential for generating and testing new hypotheses in order to propose new theories about the history of life on Earth. These include:

- Taxonomic expertise in a particular group of organisms.
- Computer literacy, the ability to work with statistical and graphical software and even the ability to design new software for specific tasks.
- Good scientific research design/technical skills and the ability to produce scientific reports for publication.

These days there is intense competition for most jobs (and PhD studentships) and this is particularly true of palaeontology. Indeed, there are far more qualified palaeontologists than there are vacancies that need filling. Hence, it is advisable to do everything you possibly can to boost your profile and secure an interview. In this regard, I cannot overstate the importance of hands-on practical experience and you should be seeking to do relevant voluntary work at the earliest possible opportunity! This may be in the form of regular museum voluntary work or as a summer intern at a museum (helping to curate collections behind the scenes or doing fossil gallery tours or specimen handling activities for the visiting public or school groups, etc.) or other institution with a palaeontology section, such as a university. Such positions are becoming more frequent these days as it is seen as an important part of outreach and public engagement. Furthermore, the ever-increasing budget cuts mean that there are fewer paid staff available to undertake all the work that needs doing.

You can also gain excellent experience on organized research trips, including palaeontological excavations. You may need to pay to attend these or at least cover the cost of your transport too and from the site, and maybe also your accommodation whilst there (unless you are in the middle of nowhere and staying in tents). The situation varies tremendously depending on whether it is being organized by a commercial entity or whether it is part of a formal research project (some institutions have summer internship programs and some even pay a daily stipend for your services). In some cases PhD students may have funding available for research assistants to help with field or lab-based elements of their research. There are lots of potential opportunities out there and it is well worth investing some time researching online to see what might be suitable for you and your future goals.

It is worth considering attending local society meetings or larger scientific conferences. You do not need to be an academic to register for a conference and it is an excellent means of getting a feel for what scientists actually do. It is also a great way of making initial contacts. Of course, if you are young and have not been to university or are in the early stages of an undergraduate degree you may find yourself out of your depth intellectually and you will certainly find yourself in the minority at such meetings, but remember that everybody at the conference was once in the same position (and probably did not have the nerve or drive to attend such events). Certainly there will be some attendees that will not want to talk to you unless it is of direct benefit to them, but on the whole palaeontologists are a friendly bunch and you will find others who are quite willing to chat with you. On a personal note, I am always impressed when I meet such individuals at conferences and try to encourage them as much as possible.

You can also make valuable contacts, keep in the loop about forthcoming events (e.g. meetings, fossil fairs, collecting trips, etc.), job vacancies, and learn a great deal about the latest palaeontological discoveries via the numerous different social media sources. Facebook has groups for just about anything you can imagine and palaeontologists from all walks of life (research, collection curation, independents, etc.) have Twitter profiles that can be followed. Pinterest boards are an excellent source for seeing great photographs of some of the best preserved fossils in the world. Make use of all the resources available to you in order to learn more about what it is you want to do ... and remember that traditional books still have a great deal to offer, even in this digital age (you are reading one right now). It is also important to read around your subject area. There is not much point in being an expert on a highly specialized topic if you are unable to contextualize your knowledge with regard to related disciplines.

That you have taken the time to read this book shows you have a passion for palaeontology. I hope I have demonstrated that you do not need to be a well-funded professional researcher in a prestigious university or museum in order to be involved with, or indeed make a significant contribution to palaeontological knowledge. You can employ transferable skills you have developed elsewhere, get free access to some electronic journals online, as well as free software packages for analysing data and making illustrations. It is all there if you look for it. I hope I have also demonstrated that there is no set route, or age, for getting into palaeontology as a career.

For the younger reader, I hope you now appreciate that palaeontology is not beyond your reach and that there is no specific road map of how to become a palaeontologist. Of course there is the traditional school–college–university route, but this is by no means the only option. Indeed, just because somebody does a PhD in palaeontology at university does not mean they will be able to make a career out of it! Hence, it is always a good idea to have a back-up plan, preferably based on transferable skills that can be applied just as well outside the field of palaeontology as within it. Nonetheless, studying the right combination of subjects throughout your education can certainly help in achieving your goal of becoming a palaeontologist and the further you go in the education system will help open different sets of doors that might otherwise be rather difficult, though not impossible, to open without a degree or PhD level qualification.

So, what is the best combination of subjects that you should be studying at school? The answer to this question will depend upon whom you ask. Most palaeontologists will agree that the traditional science subjects (biology, physics and chemistry) in addition to maths, English and geology (if available) are the most desirable, but often will prioritise them differently. My personal opinion would be to place maths and biology at the top of the list, followed by geology, chemistry and then physics (though certain branches of palaeontology, e.g. biomechanics modelling (including fluid

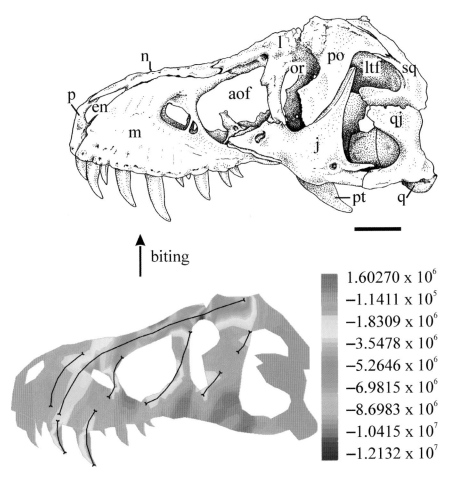

Finite element analysis as applied to the skull of a Tyrannosaurus rex to investigate bite forces relative to jaw and skull biomechanics (Benton 2010, PLoS BIOL 8(3): e1000321)

dynamics for aquatic organisms) and finite element analysis – where investigators are able to map the stresses and strains of physical actions such as biting or running onto an organism's shape – include more physics than chemistry. Regardless of the combination you choose you should be able to find a branch of palaeontology suited to your particular strengths. However, if you are planning on going via the university route, your choices should be made with your desired course entry requirements in mind! In this regard, if palaeontology is your passion then look for a university with a large and active palaeontology research group using the latest cutting edge techniques and preferably one with an affiliated museum that holds significant fossil collections.

It is also very worthwhile trying to develop a good working knowledge of basic biological statistics as early as possible (this opportunity may not arise until you start an undergraduate degree). This is a subject that many people dislike, but one that is in ever increasing demand, so if you can also add this skill to your portfolio you may just find that it is the thing that tips the balance in your favour at a job interview, particularly one that involves research.

In my experience, successful (depending on how you define this word) careers are built mainly on passion (in terms of pursuing something that is of real interest to you), self-motivated hard work and commitment (with the ability to self appraise and the flexibility to change plans as a result of this or a favourable opportunisitic circumstance), an excellent background knowledge (which can be self taught), good networking abilities and a healthy dose of luck, e.g. being in the right place at the right time … and you never know if or when that is going to happen!

In the early years of palaeontology, the fossil record was often referred to as too sparse and incomplete (including by Charles Darwin) to be particularly informative about the evolutionary history of life on Earth. We now know that this is far from true and palaeontology as a scientific discipline continues to broaden in its scope and this trend looks firmly set to continue. So, as a final thought, surely palaeontology must be the largest and most diverse of all sciences, given that it must potentially consider the majority of all species that have ever existed on Earth, over the longest possible timescales. It is now thought that life on Earth may have originated at least 4.1 billion years ago (only shortly after the planet was formed), based on the recent discovery of carbon (with a characteristic signature, a specific ratio of carbon-12 to carbon-13, that indicates the presence of photosynthetic life) contained in 4.1 billion year-old zircon from Australia. Today's biodiversity is a mere snapshot by comparison. Hence, there is clearly room and scope for anybody who wishes to make a contribution to our understanding of it. All that is left now is for me to thank you for purchasing this book and to wish you good luck in your quest!

6. Useful websites and further information

The Palaeontological Association
    www.palass.org
The Paleontological Society
    www.paleosoc.org
The International Palaeoentomological Society
    www.fossilinsects.net
The Geological Society of London
    https://www.geolsoc.org.uk
Open University Geological Society
    www.ougs.org
Palaeocast: Palaeontology podcasts
    www.palaeocast.com
Palaeontology Online
    www.palaeontologyonline.com
The palaeobiology database
    https://paleobiodb.org
Fossil insect database
    edna.palass-hosting.org
Open access journals with palaeontological content
    American Museum Novitates & Bulletin
    http://digitallibrary.amnh.org/
    ZooKeys
    zookeys.pensoft.net
    Acta Palaeontologica Polonica
    https://www.app.pan.pl
    Palaeontologia Electronica
    palaeo-electronica.org
    Paleontological Contributions
    http://paleo.ku.edu/contributions.html
    PLoS ONE
    www.plosone.org
Biodiversity Heritage Library
    www.biodiversitylibrary.org
UK fossil sites
    www.ukfossils.co.uk
    www.discoveringfossils.co.uk/locations.htm

British Geological Survey
　　www.bgs.ac.uk
UK amateur fossil hunters
　　www.ukafh.com
Rockwatch
　　www.rockwatch.org.uk
Palaeo job sites/facebook page
　　https://www.facebook.com/groups/PaleoJobs/?fref=nf
Earthworks jobs
　　http://www.earthworks-jobs.com/index.shtml
The Virtual Fossil Museum
　　www.fossilmuseum.net
The Natural History Museum, London
　　www.nhm.ac.uk
Oxford University Museum of Natural History
　　www.oum.ox.ac.uk
Sedgwick Museum of Earth Sciences (University of Cambridge)
　　www.sedgwickmuseum.org
Manchester Museum (The University of Manchester)
　　www.manchester.ac.uk/museum
Lapworth Museum of Geology
　　http://www.birmingham.ac.uk/facilities/lapworth-museum
Global Network of National Geoparks
　　http://www.globalgeopark.org/index.htm
United Nations Educational, Scientific and Cultural Organization
　　http://whc.unesco.org/
The Institute of Conservation
　　http://icon.org.uk/
The Museums Association
　　http://www.museumsassociation.org/home
The Geological Curators Group
　　www.geocurator.org
Website of the author
　　www.drdavidpenney.com

UK fossil festivals and shows (the following are just a selection)
    Lyme Regis fossil festival (usually around the May Bank Holiday)
    Scarborough fossil festival (September)
    Bakewell roch exchange, Lady Manners High School (October)
    Hampshire mineral & fossil show (September)
    Oxford mineral & fossil show, Kidlington (five times per year)

For a comprehensive list of local (and major international) societies
    http://www.ukfossils.co.uk/resources/directory.pdf

Acknowledgements
Thanks to Dean Lomax, Pete Lawrence, Richard Bizley, John Nudds, Dave Marshall and Chantal Davies for discussion and/or image permissions.

Dean Lomax presenting a signed copy of his book to Gabrielle Davies (referred to on page 14). Regardless of what you do and how you do it, one of the most important jobs is to inspire the next generation of palaeontologists!

Other titles that may be of interest
(see website for our full range of palaeontology books)

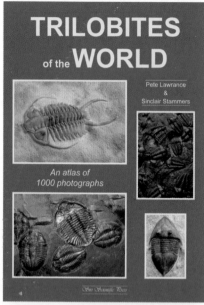

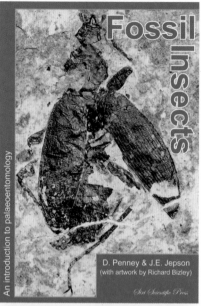

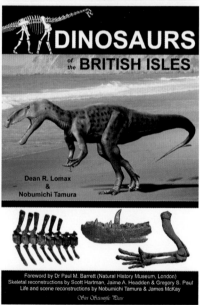

TO ORDER THESE BOOKS & SIMILAR TITLES
visit our online shop at http://www.siriscientificpress.co.uk
email: books@siriscientificpress.co.uk